C000064536

THE
ICEMAN

Published by MQ Publications Limited
12 The Ivories, 6–8 Northampton Street, London N1 2HY
Tel: 020 7359 2244 / Fax: 020 7359 1616
email: mail@mqpublications.com

ISBN: 1-84072-444-7

1 3 5 7 9 0 8 6 4 2

Printed and bound in China

THE ICEMAN
A tale of love

BY LISA SWERLING & RALPH LAZAR

HAROLD'S PLANET

MQP
MQ Publications Ltd

In a jungle of emerald, she loved all that sparkled.

Those who loved *her* knew this, and so gave her precious stones that glittered in the sunlight.

But their efforts were in vain, for she was enchanted by the jungle.

One man loved her more than any.

To win her heart,
he went in search of
something
really
special...

The iceman took it to her.

She loved it,
and so noticed him there
amongst the others.

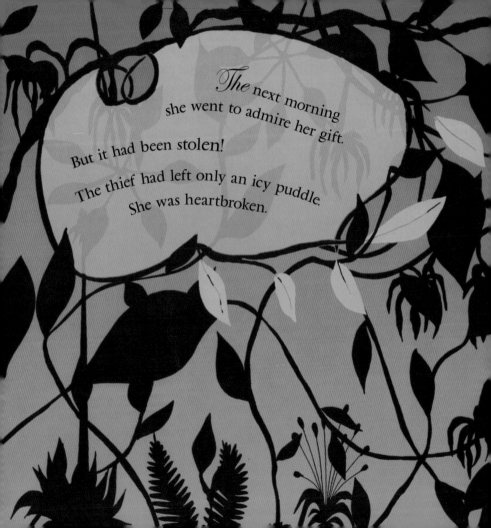

The next morning
she went to admire her gift.

But it had been stolen!

The thief had left only an icy puddle.
She was heartbroken.

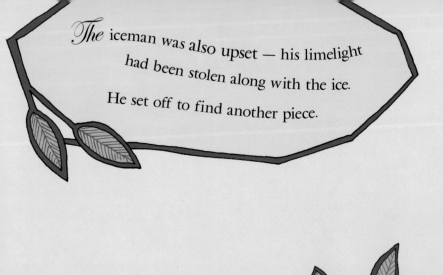

The iceman was also upset — his limelight
had been stolen along with the ice.

He set off to find another piece.

This one was even bigger.
It twinkled
like the morning dew.

That night she placed guards around her precious ice.

But overnight
the thief struck again,
leaving only an icy pool
where the gift had been.

Her sadness turned to anger.

The iceman resolved to find a piece of ice so big that no thief could steal it.

He had to journey far.

Finally he came upon an enormous block. This surely was the piece...

He set to work.

When he was done,
he began
the homeward journey.

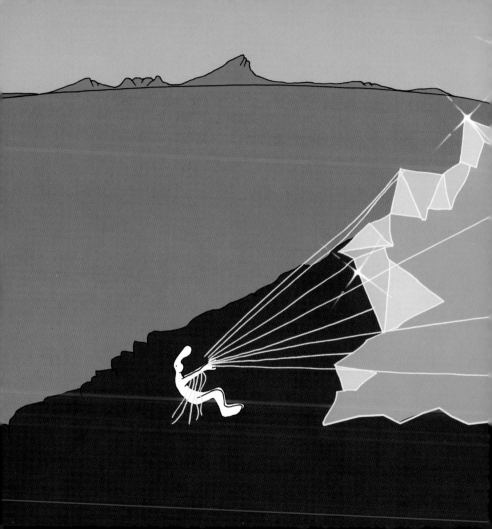

The ice was heavy...

...and soon the iceman
was too tired to move.
He collapsed beside the
giant block.

The ice stood guard,
protecting him from
the sun.

After a while it could fight the heat no more.

The water trickled past him, down towards the open plain.

Eventually the stream reached her in the jungle.

Icy to the touch! She knew at its source, she would find the thief.

She followed the stream...

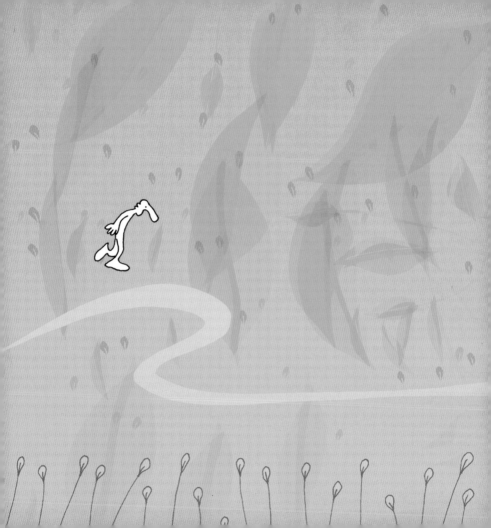

...leaving the jungle and
making her way across
the open plain.
With every step
her anger grew.

How far the thief had travelled.

Finally she reached
the last icy trickle. And there he lay.

The thief, the iceman!

$\mathcal{A}$ tiny piece of ice remained.
It sparkled as she took it in her hands...

And her heart melted too.

ABOUT THE AUTHORS

Ralph Lazar, Lisa Swerling and their daughter
Bea are currently based in the UK. They have
recently applied for visas to Harold's Planet,
and are expected to move there as soon as
the paperwork has been processed.

This book is for our parents

The End.